MAY 0 5 2011

THIS WHERE'S WALDO? BOOK BELONGS TO:

_____

_____

HEY, WALDO FANS! FIVE INTREPID TRAVELERS
ARE LOST IN EVERY SCENE! CAN YOU FIND THEM?

ODLAW   WIZARD   WENDA   WOOF   WALDO
         WHITEBEARD

AND IN EVERY SCENE, THE TRAVELERS
HAVE EACH LOST SOMETHING PRECIOUS!
CAN YOU FIND THESE ITEMS TOO?

WALDO'S KEY   WOOF'S BONE   WENDA'S CAMERA

WIZARD WHITEBEARD'S SCROLL   ODLAW'S BINOCULARS

TO ELIZABETH, MIKE, STEVE, EDDY, AND TERRY FOR ALL THEIR HELP AND ENCOURAGEMENT

First U.S. paperback edition 2007

Library of Congress Cataloging-in-Publication Data is available.
Library of Congress Catalog Card Number 91-71819

ISBN 978-0-7636-0311-3 (hardcover)

ISBN 978-0-7636-3501-5 (paperback)

09 10 11 12 13 14 WKT 12 11 10 09 08 07

Printed in Shenzhen, Guangdong, China

This book was typeset in Optima.
The illustrations were done in watercolor and water-based ink.

Candlewick Press
99 Dover Street
Somerville, MA 02144

visit us at www.candlewick.com

WHERE'S WALDO? IN HOLLYWOOD

MARTIN HANDFORD

CANDLEWICK PRESS

A DREAM COME TRUE

WOW, WALDO-WATCHERS, THIS IS FANTASTIC, I'M REALLY IN HOLLYWOOD! LOOK AT THE FILM PEOPLE EVERYWHERE – I WONDER WHAT MOVIES THEY'RE MAKING. THIS IS MY DREAM COME TRUE . . . TO MEET THE DIRECTORS AND ACTORS, TO WALK THROUGH THE CROWDS OF EXTRAS, TO SEE BEHIND THE SCENES! PHEW, I WONDER IF I'LL APPEAR IN A MOVIE MYSELF!

★ ★ ★ ★ WHAT TO LOOK FOR IN HOLLYWOOD! ★ ★ ★ ★

WELCOME TO TINSELTOWN, WALDO-WATCHERS! THESE ARE THE PEOPLE AND THINGS TO LOOK FOR AS YOU WALK THROUGH THE FILM SETS WITH WALDO.

★ FIRST (OF COURSE!) WHERE'S WALDO?

★ NEXT FIND WALDO'S CANINE COMPANION, WOOF — REMEMBER, ALL YOU CAN SEE IS HIS TAIL!

★ THEN FIND WALDO'S FRIEND WENDA!

★ ABRACADABRA! NOW FOCUS IN ON WIZARD WHITEBEARD!

★ BOO! HISS! HERE COMES THE BAD GUY, ODLAW!

★ NOW SPOT THESE 25 WALDO-WATCHERS EACH OF WHOM APPEARS ONLY ONCE BEFORE THE FINAL FANTASTIC SCENE!

★ WOW! INCREDIBLE! SPOT ONE OTHER CHARACTER WHO APPEARS IN EVERY SCENE EXCEPT THE LAST!

★ ★ KEEP ON SEARCHING! THERE'S MORE TO FIND! ★ ★

ON EVERY SET FIND WALDO'S LOST KEY

WOOF'S LOST BONE! WENDA'S LOST CAMERA! WIZARD WHITEBEARD'S SCROLL! ODLAW'S LOST BINOCULARS! AND A MISSING CAN OF FILM!

★ ★ ★ ★ ★ ★ ★ AND MORE AND MORE! ★ ★ ★ ★ ★ ★ ★

EACH OF THE FOUR POSTERS ON THE WALL OVER THERE IS PART OF ONE OF THE FILM SETS WALDO IS ABOUT TO VISIT. ★ FIND OUT WHERE THE POSTERS CAME FROM. ★ THEN SPOT ANY DIFFERENCES BETWEEN THE POSTERS AND THE SETS.

SHHH! THIS IS A SILENT MOVIE

SO THIS IS HOW THE HOLLYWOOD DREAM BEGAN – WITH SILENT MOVIES MADE IN BLACK AND WHITE. IT LOOKS CRAZY AND IT MAKES YOU LAUGH. ACTING IN SLAPSTICK COMEDIES MUST BE REALLY HARD – LOOK HOW MANY ACCIDENTS ARE HAPPENING. BUT THE GREAT THING IS THAT NONE OF THE ACTORS EVER GET HURT, HOWEVER OFTEN THEY FALL FLAT ON THEIR FACES!

$10,000

FUN IN THE FOREIGN LEGION

PHEW, MOVIE FANS. DON'T GET OVERHEATED. THIS IS THE MOST SIZZLING LOCATION SO FAR! EVERYONE'S SWELTERING, FROM STARS TO SAND-SHIFTERS. SOME OF THOSE EXTRAS LOOK LIKE THEY'RE LOSING THEIR COOL – HAVE THEY FORGOTTEN THIS IS ONLY A FILM? PERHAPS IT'S TIME A FEW MORE OF THEM DESERTED THE DESERT AND JOINED THE RUSH FOR ICE CREAM!

A TREMENDOUS SONG AND DANCE

HAVE YOU EVER SEEN SUCH AMAZING MUSICAL MAYHEM? DEFINITELY A DEAFENING SCENE OF NOTE. THAT BATTLESHIP'S STEERING CERTAINLY NEEDS FINE-TUNING! BUT LET'S NOT MAKE TOO MUCH OF A SONG AND DANCE ABOUT IT. EVEN IF THE ENTIRE CAST IS SWEPT OFF ITS FEET, THE SHOW MUST GO ON!

ALI BABA AND THE FORTY THIEVES

WHAT A CRUSH IN THE CAVE, WALDO-FOLLOWERS, BUT PAN IN ON THOSE POTS OF TREASURE! HOW MANY THIEVES WERE IN THE STORY? I BELIEVE THIS DIRECTOR THINKS FORTY THOUSAND! HAVE YOU SPOTTED ALI BABA? HE'S IN THE ALLEY, CUTTING HAIR – THE SCRIPTWRITER THINKS HIS NAME'S ALLEY BARBER! JANGLING GENIES – WHAT A FEARFULLY FUNNY FLICK THIS IS!

THE SWASHBUCKLING MUSKETEERS

ALL FOR ONE, ONE FOR ALL! – WASN'T THAT THE MOTTO OF THE THREE MUSKETEERS? NOW LOOK AT THIS FREE-FOR-ALL! CAN YOU SPOT OUR THREE GALLANT HEROES BATTLING WITH THE RED-COATED CARDINAL'S GUARDS? WITH ALL THIS SWASHBUCKLING ACTION GOING ON, I WONDER HOW THE CAMERAMEN CAN CAPTURE IT ALL ON FILM!

DINOSAURS, SPACEMEN, AND GHOULS

PHEW, INCREDIBLE! TIME, SPACE, AND HORROR ARE IN A MIGHTY MUDDLE HERE! WHAT COSMIC COSTUMES AND WHAT GREAT SPECIAL EFFECTS! ONE OF THOSE FLYING SAUCERS LOOKS LIKE IT'S REALLY FLYING! ARE THOSE REAL ALIENS INSIDE, NOT ACTORS AT ALL? SO WHAT'S REAL AND WHAT'S MADE UP IN FILMS LIKE THESE?

ROBIN HOOD'S MERRY MESS-UP

LOOK HOW MANY MERRY MEN HAVE LEFT SHERWOOD FOREST FOR A DAY OUT IN NOTTINGHAM CASTLE! AND WHAT A MERRY TIME THEY'RE HAVING, MESSING UP THE SHERIFF'S PARADE. WHICH ONE IS ROBIN HOOD? THE ONE WEARING A ROBIN HOOD, OF COURSE! WHEN YOU GO TO SEE THIS MOVIE, YOU'LL THINK IT'S ALL REAL, BUT THE CASTLE'S STONE WALLS ARE MADE OF WOOD!

WHEN THE STARS COME OUT

WOW, WALDO-WATCHERS, THIS IS WHAT I CALL GLAMOUR! I'M AT A MAJOR MOVIE PREMIERE. THE STARS HAVE COME TO SEE THE FILM: THE CROWDS HAVE COME TO SEE THE STARS. LOOK AT THAT PINK STRETCH LIMO – NOW THAT'S A PERFECT CAR FOR A STAR. AND WHO'S IN THE BONE-MOBILE BEHIND? AND DOESN'T KING KONG LOOK NICER IN LIFE THAN WHEN HE'S ON THE SCREEN?

WHERE'S WALDO? THE MUSICAL

WOW, WHAT AN EXTRAVAGANZA, WALDO-WATCHERS – THIS ALL-SINGING, ALL-DANCING MOVIE IS ALL ABOUT ME AND MY FRIENDS! LOOK HOW MANY ACTORS ARE DRESSED UP AS ME! AND LOOK AT ALL THE WOOFS, WENDAS, WIZARD WHITEBEARDS, AND ODLAWS. HAVE YOU NOTICED THAT THE WARDROBE DEPARTMENT HAS MADE MISTAKES WITH SOME OF THE ACTORS' COSTUMES? BUT THAT WON'T HELP YOU FIND THE REAL ME AND MY FOUR FRIENDS IN THIS FILM! I'LL GIVE YOU SOME CLUES. I'M THE WALDO WITH SOMETHING EXTRA FOR WOOF. ALL YOU CAN SEE OF THE REAL WOOF IS HIS TAIL. THE REAL WENDA HAS A CAMERA. THE REAL WIZARD WHITEBEARD IS WEARING A HAT BENT TO THE LEFT. AND THE REAL ODLAW IS HOLDING A WALKING STICK.
 THERE'S JUST ONE MORE THING. I'VE BEEN FOLLOWED HERE BY ONE CHARACTER FROM EVERY SET I'VE VISITED. SO CAN YOU SPOT ALL ELEVEN OF THEM IN THIS SCENE? AND CAN YOU FIND OUT WHEN EACH CHARACTER FIRST JOINED ME, AND CATCH ALL THEIR APPEARANCES THROUGHOUT MY TRAVELS?

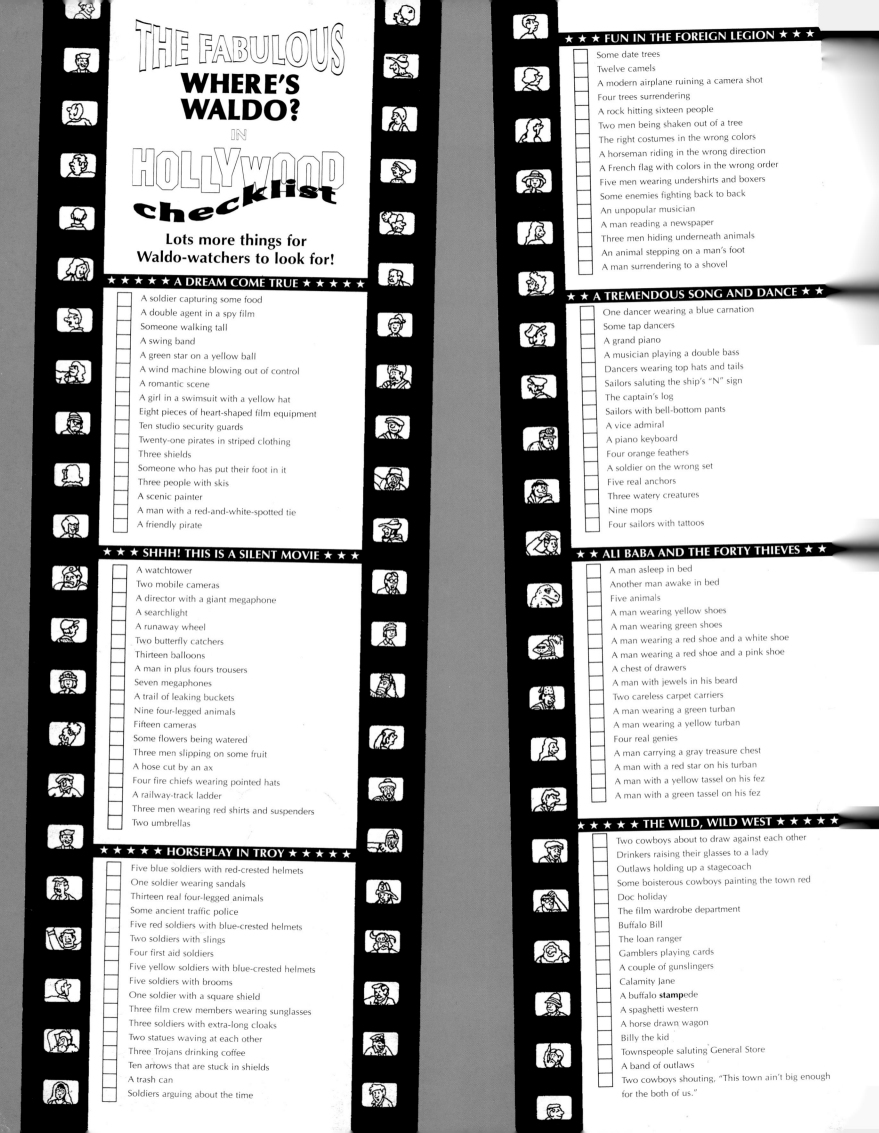

THE FABULOUS WHERE'S WALDO? IN HOLLYWOOD checklist

Lots more things for Waldo-watchers to look for!

★ ★ ★ ★ ★ A DREAM COME TRUE ★ ★ ★ ★ ★

- A soldier capturing some food
- A double agent in a spy film
- Someone walking tall
- A swing band
- A green star on a yellow ball
- A wind machine blowing out of control
- A romantic scene
- A girl in a swimsuit with a yellow hat
- Eight pieces of heart-shaped film equipment
- Ten studio security guards
- Twenty-one pirates in striped clothing
- Three shields
- Someone who has put their foot in it
- Three people with skis
- A scenic painter
- A man with a red-and-white-spotted tie
- A friendly pirate

★ ★ ★ SHHH! THIS IS A SILENT MOVIE ★ ★ ★

- A watchtower
- Two mobile cameras
- A director with a giant megaphone
- A searchlight
- A runaway wheel
- Two butterfly catchers
- Thirteen balloons
- A man in plus fours trousers
- Seven megaphones
- A trail of leaking buckets
- Nine four-legged animals
- Fifteen cameras
- Some flowers being watered
- Three men slipping on some fruit
- A hose cut by an ax
- Four fire chiefs wearing pointed hats
- A railway-track ladder
- Three men wearing red shirts and suspenders
- Two umbrellas

★ ★ ★ ★ ★ HORSEPLAY IN TROY ★ ★ ★ ★ ★

- Five blue soldiers with red-crested helmets
- One soldier wearing sandals
- Thirteen real four-legged animals
- Some ancient traffic police
- Five red soldiers with blue-crested helmets
- Two soldiers with slings
- Four first aid soldiers
- Five yellow soldiers with blue-crested helmets
- Five soldiers with brooms
- One soldier with a square shield
- Three film crew members wearing sunglasses
- Three soldiers with extra-long cloaks
- Two statues waving at each other
- Three Trojans drinking coffee
- Ten arrows that are stuck in shields
- A trash can
- Soldiers arguing about the time

★ ★ ★ FUN IN THE FOREIGN LEGION ★ ★ ★

- Some date trees
- Twelve camels
- A modern airplane ruining a camera shot
- Four trees surrendering
- A rock hitting sixteen people
- Two men being shaken out of a tree
- The right costumes in the wrong colors
- A horseman riding in the wrong direction
- A French flag with colors in the wrong order
- Five men wearing undershirts and boxers
- Some enemies fighting back to back
- An unpopular musician
- A man reading a newspaper
- Three men hiding underneath animals
- An animal stepping on a man's foot
- A man surrendering to a shovel

★ ★ A TREMENDOUS SONG AND DANCE ★ ★

- One dancer wearing a blue carnation
- Some tap dancers
- A grand piano
- A musician playing a double bass
- Dancers wearing top hats and tails
- Sailors saluting the ship's "N" sign
- The captain's log
- Sailors with bell-bottom pants
- A vice admiral
- A piano keyboard
- Four orange feathers
- A soldier on the wrong set
- Five real anchors
- Three watery creatures
- Nine mops
- Four sailors with tattoos

★ ★ ALI BABA AND THE FORTY THIEVES ★ ★

- A man asleep in bed
- Another man awake in bed
- Five animals
- A man wearing yellow shoes
- A man wearing green shoes
- A man wearing a red shoe and a white shoe
- A man wearing a red shoe and a pink shoe
- A chest of drawers
- A man with jewels in his beard
- Two careless carpet carriers
- A man wearing a green turban
- A man wearing a yellow turban
- Four real genies
- A man carrying a gray treasure chest
- A man with a red star on his turban
- A man with a yellow tassel on his fez
- A man with a green tassel on his fez

★ ★ ★ ★ THE WILD, WILD WEST ★ ★ ★ ★

- Two cowboys about to draw against each other
- Drinkers raising their glasses to a lady
- Outlaws holding up a stagecoach
- Some boisterous cowboys painting the town red
- Doc holiday
- The film wardrobe department
- Buffalo Bill
- The loan ranger
- Gamblers playing cards
- A couple of gunslingers
- Calamity Jane
- A buffalo **stamp**ede
- A spaghetti western
- A horse drawn wagon
- Billy the kid
- Townspeople saluting General Store
- A band of outlaws
- Two cowboys shouting, "This town ain't big enough for the both of us."

★ ★ THE SWASHBUCKLING MUSKETEERS ★ ★

- [ ] Eleven gentlemen bowing
- [ ] Two wheelbarrows
- [ ] Twelve spouts of water
- [ ] A tear-jerking emotional scene
- [ ] A gentleman with only one glove
- [ ] Three musket tears
- [ ] One lost glove
- [ ] A man wearing different colored gloves
- [ ] A hat with a striped plume
- [ ] Badly dressed men turned away from the dance
- [ ] A bouncer
- [ ] Three angry gardeners
- [ ] Two swordsmen fencing
- [ ] Three mixed-up statues
- [ ] A man having his foot tickled
- [ ] Four ladies being presented with flowers
- [ ] Four real animals

★ DINOSAURS, SPACEMEN, AND GHOULS ★

- [ ] "Hand" luggage
- [ ] A fly in saucer
- [ ] A ticklish dinosaur
- [ ] A greedy green alien
- [ ] A dozing dinosaur
- [ ] A spaceship
- [ ] A smart-alecky dinosaur
- [ ] Stars in a star's dressing room
- [ ] A wolfman having a howling good time
- [ ] Eight characters in craters
- [ ] A planet picnic
- [ ] A game of ringtoss
- [ ] A space castle
- [ ] Two people reading books
- [ ] Four cavemen going up in the world
- [ ] An astronaut without helmet, gloves, or boots
- [ ] Two bottles of ketchup

★ ★ ROBIN HOOD'S MERRY MESS-UP ★ ★

- [ ] Eight ladies in medieval costume
- [ ] "Little" John leading some men
- [ ] Sixteen flags
- [ ] Two archers with long bows
- [ ] "Maid" Marian cleaning up
- [ ] A medieval extra with a radio
- [ ] A sheriff's soldier with rolled-up sleeves
- [ ] "Fryer" Tuck
- [ ] A night in armor
- [ ] A knight with a pink plume in his helmet
- [ ] The Sheriff of Nottingham
- [ ] A man with a bow and arrow
- [ ] A soldier with a large shield
- [ ] Medieval soldiers wearing the wrong pants
- [ ] A prisoner with a giant ball and chain
- [ ] Five real four-legged animals
- [ ] Twenty-one ladders
- [ ] Seven helmets with animal crests

★ ★ ★ WHEN THE STARS COME OUT ★ ★ ★

- [ ] Twenty-nine lights
- [ ] Two rival news reporters
- [ ] Someone who has it all wrapped up
- [ ] A policeman wanting an autograph
- [ ] Three cowboys
- [ ] Ten hearts
- [ ] Seven large palms
- [ ] Someone with a bird's-eye view
- [ ] A handful of spectators
- [ ] A celebrity wearing a new dress
- [ ] Someone making their mark
- [ ] Two astronauts
- [ ] A sleepy spectator with an alarm clock
- [ ] A twisting telescope
- [ ] An extra-long straw
- [ ] Four celebrities wearing sunglasses

★ ★ ★ WHERE'S WALDO? THE MUSICAL ★ ★ ★

- [ ] A Waldo sweater with stripes in reverse order
- [ ] A Waldo with blond hair
- [ ] A Waldo with a beard
- [ ] A Wenda without any shoes
- [ ] A Waldo wearing shades
- [ ] An Odlaw without a mustache
- [ ] A Waldo sweater with extra stripes
- [ ] A haredresser
- [ ] A Waldo wearing a hat without a bobble
- [ ] A Waldo without pockets on his jeans
- [ ] A Wizard Whitebeard wearing glasses
- [ ] A Waldo script reading
- [ ] A sound mixer
- [ ] A Wenda with a blue-and-white-striped umbrella
- [ ] A walking stick
- [ ] Two Wizard Whitebeards without beards
- [ ] A Waldo without glasses
- [ ] An Odlaw wearing a hat without a bobble
- [ ] A Wenda with blonde hair
- [ ] A Waldo wearing a bobble hat in reverse colors
- [ ] A Wenda without glasses
- [ ] A Wizard Whitebeard wearing a red hat
- [ ] A Woof wearing a bobble hat in reverse colors
- [ ] A Wenda wearing round Waldo glasses
- [ ] A Waldo tickling another Waldo
- [ ] A Woof without a bobble hat
- [ ] A Wenda with no pockets on her skirt
- [ ] A Waldo holding a walking stick the wrong way up
- [ ] A Woof wearing a hat without a bobble
- [ ] A Woof wearing shades
- [ ] A back view of a Wenda
- [ ] A Waldo in blue-and-white stripes
- [ ] A Wenda who is not wearing a bobble hat
- [ ] An Odlaw without shades
- [ ] A Wizard Whitebeard dancing
- [ ] A back view of a Waldo
- [ ] A Wizard Whitebeard wearing a bobble hat
- [ ] A Woof wearing a blue-and-white bobble hat
- [ ] Two Wizard Whitebeards without white beards
- [ ] A Wenda wearing a hat without a bobble
- [ ] A Waldo with two bobble hats

★ ★ ★ ★ BACK TO THE BEGINNING ★ ★ ★ ★

Did you find Waldo, all his friends, and all the things they lost? Did you find the mystery character who appears in every scene except the last? And one more thing: Somewhere one of the Waldo-watchers lost the bobble from his hat. Can you spot which one and find the bobble?

Don't go away! The game's not over yet! Go right back to the beginning and look closely at the golden Waldo trophies! Ten of them are different from the rest—can you tell which ones?

★ ★ ★ ★ ★ THE FINAL FILM TEST ★ ★ ★ ★ ★

Nearly all the faces in the sprocket holes on this and the facing page appear in color somewhere else in the book. Can you find where? But . . . ten of them do *not* appear anywhere else! Can you tell which ten? Lastly . . . some faces appear more than once in the sprocket holes. Can you see which ones and how many times each one appears?

★ ★ ★ ★ ★ ★ ★ ★ ★ ★ ★ ★ ★ ★ ★ ★ ★ ★ ★

WHERE'S WALDO?
IN
HOLLYWOOD

THE END

THE WHERE'S WALDO? COLLECTION

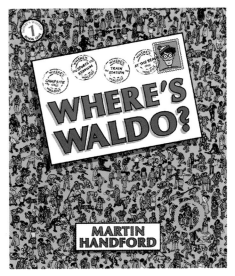

Down the road, over the sea, around the globe . . . Where's Waldo? on his worldwide adventures!

ISBN 978-0-7636-3498-8

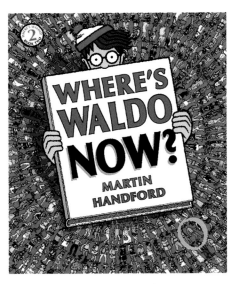

Over thousands of years, past thousands of people . . . Where's Waldo? now!

ISBN 978-0-7636-3499-5

Once upon a mermaid, once upon a dragon . . . Where's Waldo? in the realms of fantasy!

ISBN 978-0-7636-3500-8

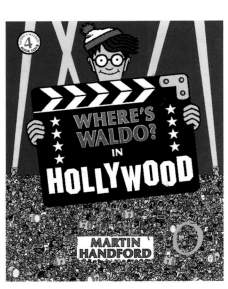

Lights, camera, action! Where's Waldo? behind the scenes!

ISBN 978-0-7636-3501-5

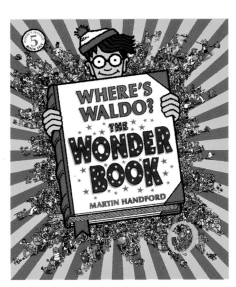

Stepping off the pages and into life . . . Where's Waldo? in lands full of wonder!

ISBN 978-0-7636-3502-2

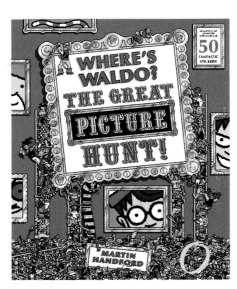

Pick a sticker, spot the difference, match the silhouettes . . . Where's Waldo? at the gallery!

ISBN 978-0-7636-3043-0

Have you found all six Waldo books yet?